This

Buttons Family

book belongs to

_____

_____

Cherry and Charlie and Baby Lou,

We're the Buttons, we're just like you!

And every day there's something new

For Cherry and Charlie and Baby Lou!

First published 2012 by Walker Books Ltd
87 Vauxhall Walk, London SE11 5HJ

10 9 8 7 6 5 4 3 2 1

Text © 2012 Vivian French
Illustrations © 2012 Sue Heap

The right of Vivian French and Sue Heap to be identified as
author and illustrator respectively of this work has been
asserted by them in accordance with the Copyright, Designs
and Patents Act 1988

This book has been typeset in HVD Bodedo

Printed in China

British Library Cataloguing in
Publication Data: a catalogue record
for this book is available from
the British Library

ISBN 978-1-4063-2857-8

www.walker.co.uk

The Buttons Family
Going to the Doctor

✚

Vivian French

illustrated by
Sue Heap

WALKER BOOKS
AND SUBSIDIARIES
LONDON · BOSTON · SYDNEY · AUCKLAND

"Cherry keeps
sneezing,"
said Charlie.

"No, I don't,"
said Cherry.
"Sneezy," giggled
Baby Lou.

"My throat hurts," Cherry complained. "It's a bit red," said Mum. "We'd better go to the doctor."

"Doctors are scary," said Charlie.
Mum phoned the surgery while
Charlie counted
Cherry's sneezes.

15! 16!

ATISHOO

"Let's go," said Mum.
"Do I HAVE to?"
Cherry asked.

Charlie and Baby Lou made
ambulance noises all the
way to the doctor's.

At the surgery, the lady behind the desk asked them to take a seat in the waiting room.

"I want to go home," wailed Cherry. "I know," said Mum. "But if you watch what Dr Marsh does, when you get home you can play doctors."

Cherry cheered up. "And I'LL be the doctor," she said.

Mum had to read three stories before Cherry's name was called.

Charlie rushed into Dr Marsh's room. "Cherry's got the sneezes!" he said.

"Sneezy," said Baby Lou. "And a sore throat," said Charlie. "SHH!" Cherry frowned. "It's ME that's ill."

"Cherry, can you open your mouth very wide?" said Dr Marsh. She looked inside with a little torch.

"Oh, poor you. It does look sore."

"What's that?" Charlie asked. "It's a stethoscope," said Dr Marsh. "It's for listening to Cherry's chest."

"Now, Cherry, take a deep breath." Dr Marsh listened.
"You're a little bit wheezy."

"Would you like to hear
your heart beat?"
Cherry put the ear pieces into
her ears, and Dr Marsh
held the metal disc against
her chest.

"My heart's going 'Oompa oompa oompa!'" said Cherry.

Dr Marsh gave Mum
a piece of paper.

"Here's a prescription for some medicine.

Cherry should take it three times a day. Come back if she gets any worse."

"We're going home to play doctors," said Cherry, "and I'm going to be the doctor." Dr Marsh laughed.

"I hope your patients are as good as you!"

"See?" said Cherry. "Doctors aren't scary."

"Who said they were?" said Charlie. "They're great!" "Sneezy," said Baby Lou, and she sneezed an **enormous** sneeze.

ATISHOO

There are six **Buttons Family** books to collect.
Which ones have you read?

New Shoes

Charlie's shoes are too tight!
He says he doesn't want
new ones, but what do
his toes say?

ISBN 978-1-4063-2855-4

Going to
the Doctor

Cherry's got a nasty cold.
How will Mum persuade
her to go to the doctor?

ISBN 978-1-4063-2857-8

Staying with Gran

Cherry, Charlie and Baby Lou have
never stayed with Gran on their
own before. Will Gran make sure
they feel at home?

ISBN 978-1-4063-2860-8

First Day
at Playschool

It's Cherry's first day
at playschool and she's
feeling a little shy.
How will she settle in?

ISBN 978-1-4063-2856-1

The
Babysitter

Mum and Dad are going out.
What do Cherry, Charlie
and Baby Lou think of the
new babysitter?

ISBN 978-1-4063-2858-5

Going to
the Dentist

It's time for the Buttons
to go to the dentist!
How will they get on at
their check-up?

ISBN 978-1-4063-2859-2

Available from all good booksellers